MW01012805

Ten Little Sandpipers

Published by Lucky Four Press, LLC, 2021

Library of Congress Control Number: 2021904918

All inquiries should be directed to: luckyfourpress@yahoo.com
or to the author at: kim@kimann.co.

ISBN-13: 978-1-953774-01-9 Paperback
ISBN-13: 978-1-953774-00-2 Hardback

www.kimann.co

Ten Little Sandpipers

A Counting Book

Kim Ann ♡

Written by Kim Ann

Illustrated by Nejla Shojaie

One happy little sandpiper
is resting in the sand.
A wave is bringing lots of water.
Quick! Go near the land!

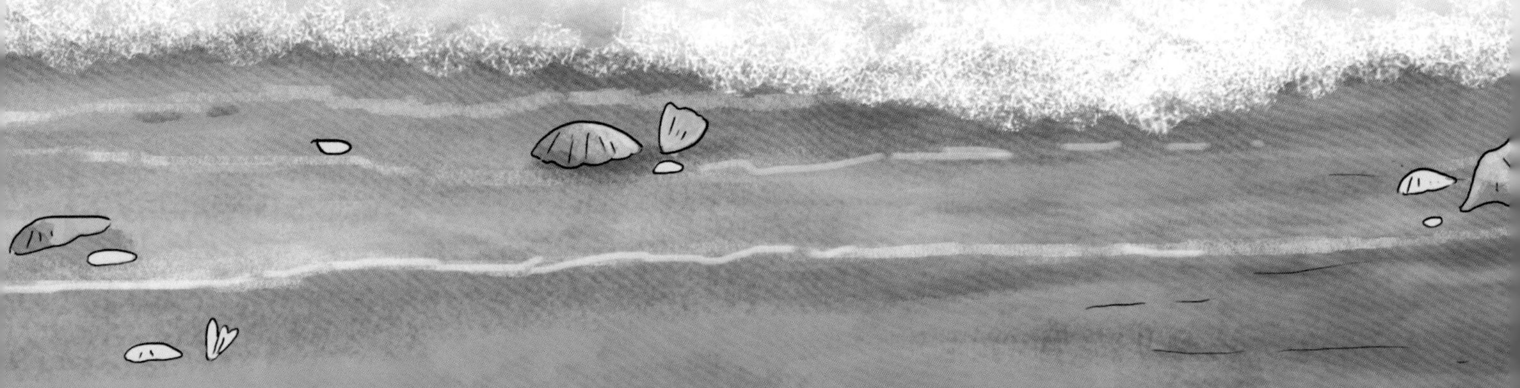

Two playful little sandpipers
are heading for a wave.
Be careful now. You'll both get wet!
The waves can misbehave!

Three tiny little sandpipers
are standing in a row.
Come on, let's find a place to play.
Get ready, set, and go!

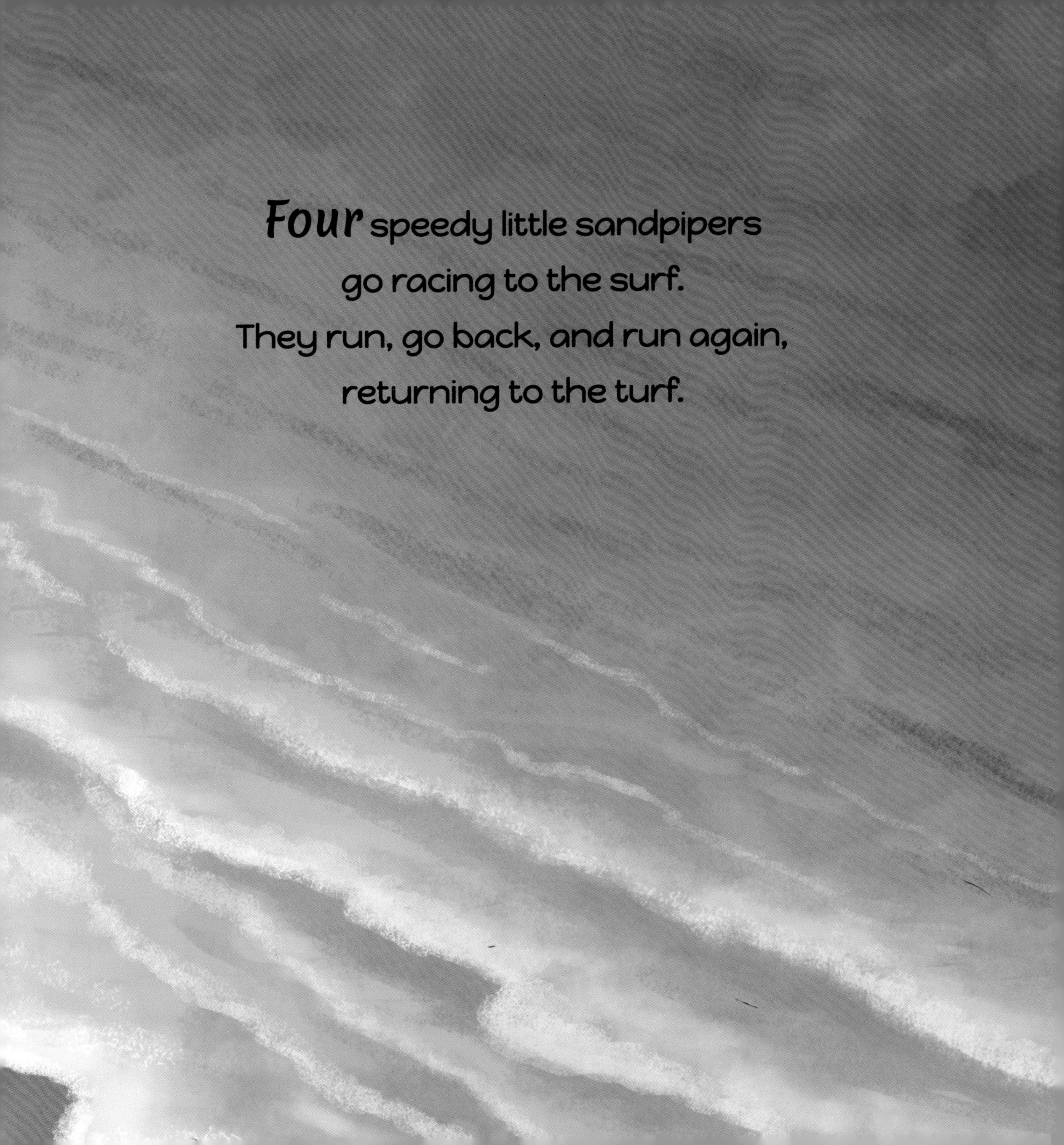

Four speedy little sandpipers
go racing to the surf.
They run, go back, and run again,
returning to the turf.

Five friendly little sandpipers—
together they belong.
They try to join each other
when they run or walk along.

Six precious little sandpipers
go one behind the other.
They're standing close with open eyes
and learning from their mother.

Seven little sandpipers
are playing catch and run.
They're quickly looking for a snack
while also having fun.

Eight fluffy little sandpipers
have feathers white and gray.
They live beside the ocean,
where they grow and thrive and play.

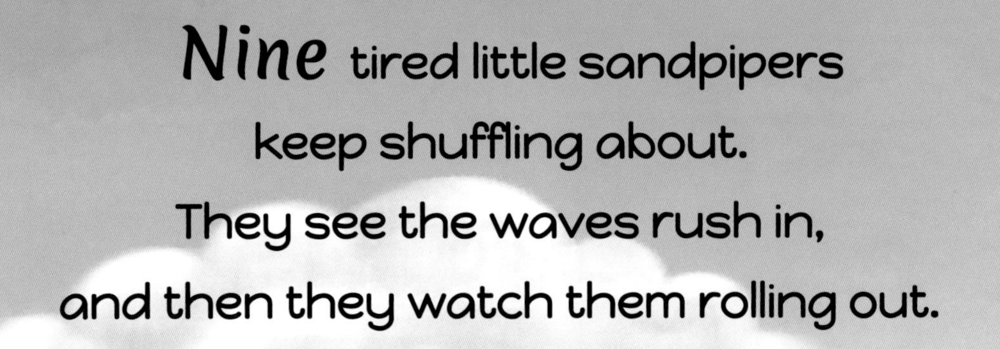

Nine tired little sandpipers
keep shuffling about.
They see the waves rush in,
and then they watch them rolling out.

Ten sleepy little sandpipers
run fast throughout the day.
Back and forth, they shuffle
'til the tide has gone away.

Mom and Dad sandpipers both take care of the eggs.
Sandpipers are most active during the day.

Sandpipers change their colors when trying to impress others.
Sandpipers fly together when they are scared.

Find the following items and

count one to five!

1 sandpiper
2 dolphins in the water
3 crabs
4 starfish
5 seashells

How many crabs can you spot in the book?

Download the song and sing along!

Featured Titles

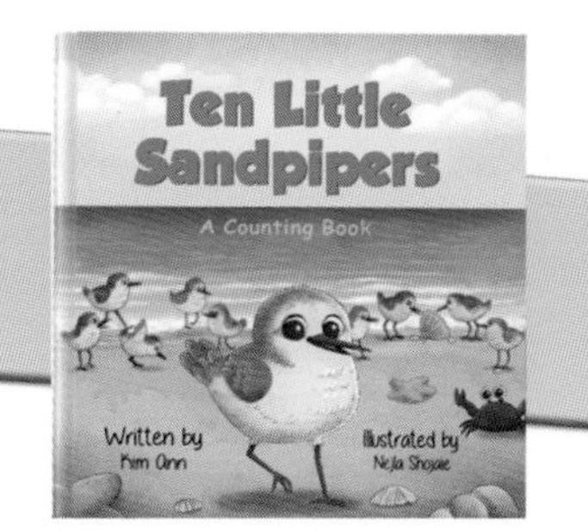
Ten Little Sandpipers
A Counting Book
Written by Kim Ann
Illustrated by Nejla Shojaie

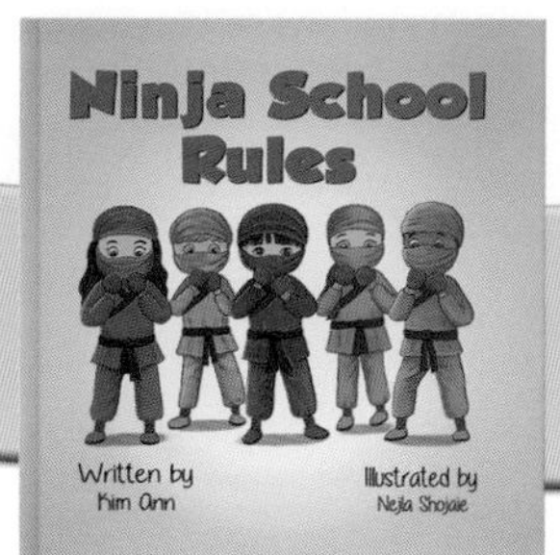
Ninja School Rules
Written by Kim Ann
Illustrated by Nejla Shojaie

If you enjoyed this book, check out these other titles by author Kim Ann!

www.kimann.co

Ruby the Rainbow Witch
A Picture-Perfect Rainbow Day
by Kim Ann

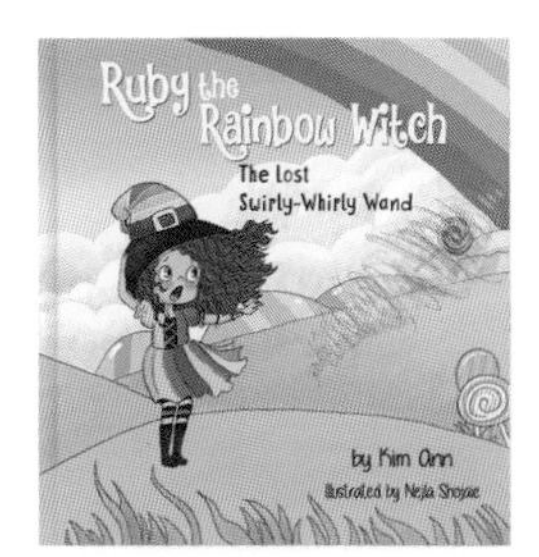
Ruby the Rainbow Witch
The Lost Swirly-Whirly Wand
by Kim Ann
Illustrated by Nejla Shojaie

Ruby the Rainbow Witch
Meet the Amber Fairies
by Kim Ann
Illustrated by Nejla Shojaie

Ruby the Rainbow Witch
Let's Color
by Kim Ann
Illustrated by Nejla Shojaie

Goldy the Puppy and the Missing Socks
by Kim Ann
Illustrated by Nejla Shojaie

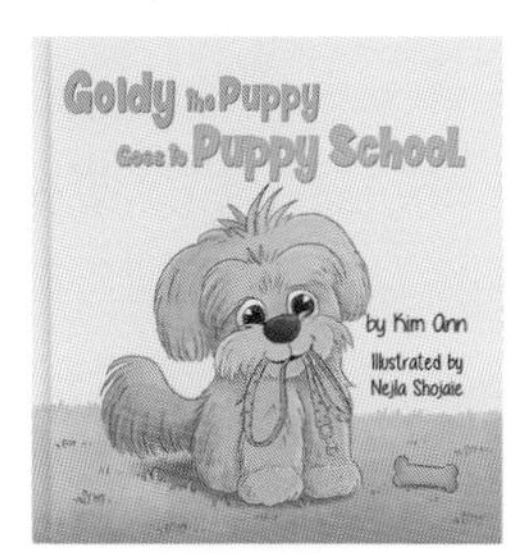
Goldy the Puppy Goes to Puppy School
by Kim Ann
Illustrated by Nejla Shojaie

Goldy the Puppy and the Birthday Spa Day
by Kim Ann
Illustrated by Nejla Shojaie

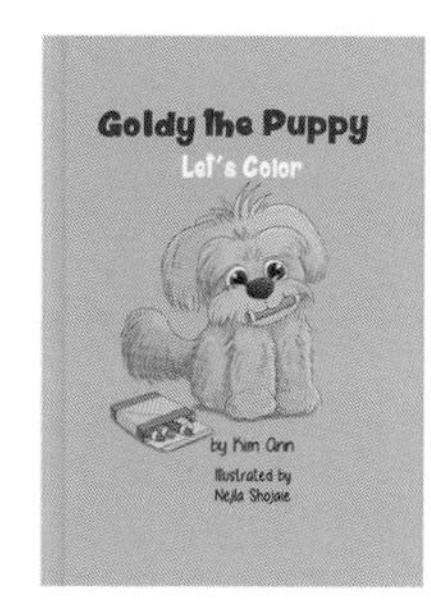
Goldy the Puppy
Let's Color
by Kim Ann
Illustrated by Nejla Shojaie

Where Do Elves Go on Vacation
by Kim Ann
Illustrated by Nejla Shojaie

Where Does Santa Go on Vacation?
by Kim Ann
Illustrated by Nejla Shojaie

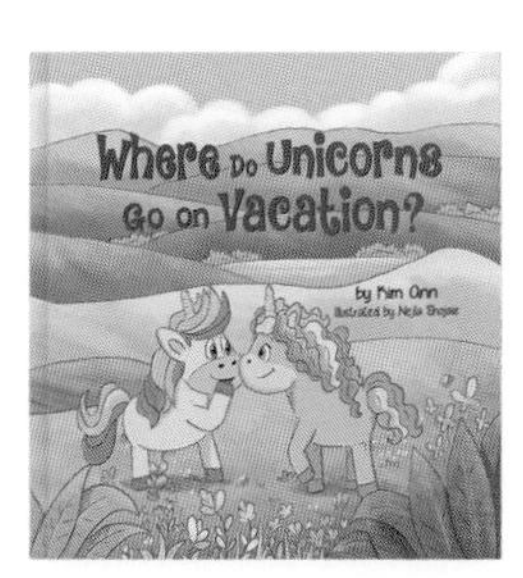
Where Do Unicorns Go on Vacation?
by Kim Ann
Illustrated by Nejla Shojaie

Where Do Dinosaurs Go on Vacation?
by Kim Ann
Illustrated by Nejla Shojaie

Where Do Mermaids Go on Vacation?
by Kim Ann
Illustrated by Nejla Shojaie